mrBean™

Royal Bean

tigeraspect
PRODUCTIONS
an endemol company

Popcorn
ELT
Readers

Meet ...
the people in

mr Bean™

Mr Bean
This is Mr Bean. He likes the Queen.

The Queen
This is the Queen. She loves dogs.

Teddy
This is Mr Bean's teddy. Mr Bean loves Teddy.

The Queen's butler

This is the Queen's butler. He works in Buckingham Palace.

Buckingham Palace

This is Buckingham Palace. The Queen lives here.

The Queen's dog

This is the Queen's favourite dog. He likes teddies!

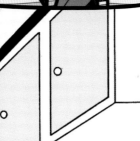

Before you read ...
Do you like animals? What animal is in the story?

New Words

What do these new words mean? Ask your teacher or use your dictionary.

mug

This is my **mug**.

bone

Dogs like **bones**.

royal

The Queen lives in this palace. It is a **royal** palace.

lorry

This **lorry** is red.

shop

This is my favourite **shop**.

shop assistant

He is a **shop assistant**.

toast

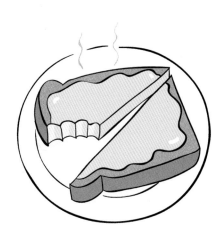

This **toast** is nice!

tea

My mum likes **tea**.

'Woof!'

Woof!

Woof! Woof!

THE WORLD OF BEAN

Let's meet Mr Bean and ask him some questions ...

 Q Hello, Mr Bean! How are you?

 A I'm fine. I'm watching TV.

Q What do you do at the weekend, Mr Bean?

A I watch TV and read and watch TV and sleep and watch TV.

 Q Do you like TV?

 A Yes, because *I'm* on TV!

Q Who is your best friend?

A My best friend is Teddy.

Q Where does Teddy come from?

A A shop, of course!

Q Do you like animals, Mr Bean?

A Yes. I do. I like elephants.

Q Have you got animals at home?

A No, I haven't. I can't have an elephant because my house is very small.

– Thank you, Mr Bean. Goodbye!

– Goodbye!

What do these words mean? Find out.
question   weekend   elephant

Royal Bean

It is morning. Mr Bean is in the kitchen.

Mr Bean is making breakfast.

I'm hungry.

Now he is looking for something.

Look! It's my favourite mug.

ROYAL MUG

Your Majesty!*

* You say *Your Majesty* to the Queen.

8

Mr Bean has got a bag.

BANG!

Good morning!

YES?

Have you got this mug?

12

The Queen's dog is in front of Mr Bean's car.

He's there!

Woof! Woof!

Go away!

The dog goes away.

Mr Bean goes after the lorry again.

Where's the lorry now?

It's here!

This is the mug shop at Buckingham Palace.

Let's go in, Teddy.

The dog is there again!

Woof! Woof!

The dog wants Teddy.

Stop! Horrible dog!

Now go away!

Mr Bean goes into the shop.

Look! My favourite mug!

The dog is in the shop too!

Oh no!

The dog has got Teddy.

Where is the dog going?

18

Where is Mr Bean now?

Ha, ha! He can't see me.

Woof!

What's that?

It's the dog and Teddy!

Stop that dog!

The butler can see Mr Bean.

Suddenly a door opens.

21

22

Who is this?

La, la, la!

Mr Bean is behind the picture.

Teddy, this is good!

Woof! Woof!

Woof!

No! You can't have Teddy!

Who's there?

Mr Bean is looking at the Queen's mug.

It's my favourite mug too!

My favourite mug!

Next day, Mr Bean goes to Buckingham Palace again.

This is for you. Thank you, Mr Bean!

Woof! Woof!

THE END

25

Real World

Buckingham Palace

Buckingham Palace is the Queen's home in London. Let's read more about it.

How many tourists go to Buckingham Palace?

Tourists can go to the Palace in the summer. 50,000 tourists go every year. They can see some of the Queen's rooms and pictures.

How many rooms are there?

Buckingham Palace has 775 rooms. There are 240 bedrooms and 78 bathrooms!

Queen Elizabeth II

Has the Palace got a garden?

Yes, there's a big garden behind the Palace. In the summer, the Queen has parties in the garden. At a garden party, there are 8,000 guests. The guests drink 27,000 cups of tea and eat 20,000 slices of cake.

corgi dog

slice of cake

Do animals live in the Palace?

Yes, the Queen likes dogs. She has got seven corgi dogs and they live in the Palace too.

What do these words mean?
tourist   bathroom
party / parties   guest   cup

★
Do you know a palace in your country?
★

After you read

1 Yes or No? Read and circle.

a) Mr Bean eats toast for breakfast. (Yes) No
b) Mr Bean likes his mug. Yes No
c) The shop assistant is very quiet. Yes No
d) The Queen likes dogs. Yes No
e) The dog wants Teddy. Yes No
f) Mr Bean likes the dog. Yes No
g) Mr Bean goes to Buckingham Yes No
   Palace in a lorry.

2 Match the characters to the descriptions.

a) The Queen   i) It has got four legs.
  It lives in Buckingham Palace.
b) Mr Bean   ii) She likes singing.
  She lives in Buckingham Palace.
c) The dog   iii) He works in Buckingham Palace.
  He has got black hair.
d) The butler   iv) He has got a green car.
  He likes Teddy.

Where's the popcorn?
Look in your book.
Can you find it?

Puzzle time!

1 What is this?

a) ....dog.............

b) ....

c) ....

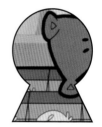

d) ....

e) ....

2 Look and write.

I'm sad.   ~~I'm happy.~~   I'm angry.

a)

I'm happy.

b)

....

c)

....

3 Complete the crossword and answer the question.

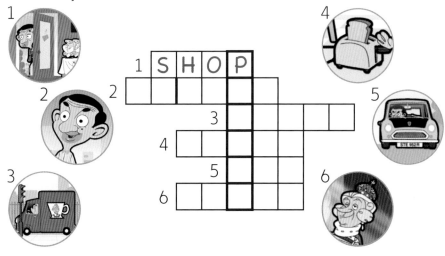

Where does the Queen live? In the P__ __ __ __ __

4 Match and circle the word.

a) The butler has got a (mug) / bone.

b) The Queen has got a **dog** / **teddy**.

c) The dog has got a **teddy** / **bone**.

d) Mr Bean has got a **mug** / **teddy**.

30

Imagine ...

1 Work in pairs. Practise the dialogue.

Mr Bean Your Majesty!
Queen Hello, who are you?
Mr Bean I'm Mr Bean.
Queen Thank you, Mr Bean!
Mr Bean Your Majesty, please, please, please can I have a mug?
Queen Yes, of course, Mr Bean.
Mr Bean Thank you, your Majesty!

2 You have two minutes. Say the dialogue with as many friends as you can.

Chant

1 🎵 Listen and read.

Let's go to London!

Hi, everyone! I'm Mr Bean!
Let's go to London
And see the Queen!

Let's go in my car.
It's not very far.
Are you ready?
Don't sit on Teddy!

Hi everyone! I'm Mr Bean!
Let's go to London
And see the Queen!

2 🎵 Say the chant.